REVISE EDEXCEL
FUNCTIONAL SKILLS ENTRY LEVEL

English

REVISION WORKBOOK

Series Consultant: Harry Smith

Author: David Grant

- -

To revise all the topics covered in this book, check out:

Revise Functional Skills Entry Level 3
English Revision Guide   978 1 292 20711 7

THE REVISE SERIES
For the full range of Pearson revision titles, visit:
www.pearsonschools.co.uk/revise

Contents

1-to-1
page match with the
Entry Level 3 Revision
Guide
ISBN 978 129220 711 7

A small bit of small print

Edexcel publishes Sample Test Materials on its website. This is the official content and this book should be used in conjunction with it. The questions in this book have been written to help you practise what you have learned in your revision. Remember: the real test questions may not look like this.

Your reading test

1   How many tasks will you need to complete in the reading test? Put a tick ☑ in the correct box.

☐ **A** one

☐ **B** two

☐ **C** three

☐ **D** four

2   Complete the following sentence by filling in the missing word.

For each of the tasks in my reading test, I will have to read .... texts.

3   What should you do at the end of the test when you have finished answering the questions?

....

....

4   List **three** things you should look for when checking your work.

....

....

....

5   How long will you be given to complete the reading test? Put a tick ☑ in the correct box.

☐ **A** 30 minutes

☐ **B** 45 minutes

☐ **C** 1 hour

☐ **D** 1 hour 30 minutes

6   List **two** things you could use a dictionary for in the reading test.

....

....

....

Reading the question

1   In each of the test-style questions below, circle the words that tell you in which text you can find the correct answer.

---

5   According to Text A2, at what age did Jules Jardine begin designing clothes for her friends?

(1 mark)

6   According to Text B2, on which date will Ula arrive in Barcelona?

(1 mark)

7   According to Text B1, where do coaches to Barcelona depart from?

(1 mark)

---

2   Putting a question into your own words can help you to find the correct answer. Look again at question 5 above. Which of the questions below has exactly the same meaning as question 5? Put a tick ☑ in the correct box.

☐ **A** What does it say in Text A2 about Jules Jardine designing clothes for her friends?

☐ **B** In Text A2, how old was Jules Jardine when she began designing clothes for her friends?

☐ **C** How old were Jules Jardine's friends when she began designing clothes, according to Text A2?

☐ **D** In Text A2, when Jules Jardine began designing old clothes, how old were they?

▷**GUIDED**▷ 3   Look again at question 6 above. Rewrite the question using your own words.

In Text B2, what will be the date when ....

....

4   Look again at question 7 above. Rewrite the question using your own words.

....

....

Had a go ☐   Nearly there ☐   Nailed it! ☐

Finding the main idea

GUIDED 1   Which **three** parts of a text can be useful in helping you to work out the main idea?

The most useful parts are the introduction, the title and ....

....

Look at this extract from Text A1, then answer questions 2 and 3.

Text A1

Jamie sees a notice in his local newspaper.

Westerby College Enterprise Day

Come and join us at Westerby College on Friday 4th March for an Enterprise Day. Get some help and information about how to find work and how to start your own business.

---

2   What type of text is Text A1? Circle the correct answer.

website   notice   letter   email   advert

GUIDED 3   What is the main idea of this text?

This text gives the reader information about ....

....

....

Now, read the introduction, title and first sentence of Text B1 on page 52.

4   What type of text is Text B1?

....

5   What is the main idea of this text?

....

....

....

Underlining key words

1   Look at the advice below. In what order should you follow these three pieces of advice to find the correct answers to questions in the reading test? Order them 1, 2, and 3.

☐   Read around the key word or phrase in the text to find the answer.

☐   Identify a key word or phrase in the question.

☐   Skim read the text to find the key word or phrase you have identified in the question.

2   Look at the test-style question below. Circle the key words or phrases in the question.

> According to Text B1, what kind of people will think that Barcelona is the perfect city break?
>
> **(1 mark)**

3   Read the following extract from Text B1 and circle the key words or phrases you identified in question 2.

Text B1

Holiday Time!

Take a coach trip to beautiful Barcelona

Home

Hotels

Flights

Barcelona is a beautiful city with thousands of things to see and do. It's the perfect city break if you want sun, sea and sight-seeing.

4   Now, read the sentence in the extract that contains the key words or phrases. Use the information you have found to answer the following question.

> According to Text B1, what kind of people will think that Barcelona is the perfect city break? Put a tick ☑ in the correct box.
>
> ☐   **A**   people who want sun, sea and sight-seeing
>
> ☐   **B**   people who enjoy art galleries and shopping
>
> ☐   **C**   people who love eating delicious food
>
> ☐   **D**   people who like visiting beautiful cities
>
> **(1 mark)**

Finding details

> **GUIDED**   1   Look at this test-style question. The key word or phrase in the question has been circled to help you.

> According to Text C2, Jen has been (invited to an interview) for which job?
>
> **(1 mark)**

Read the sentences from Text C2 below. Sentence 'B' contains the key phrase from the question above, but which sentence contains the answer? Put a tick ☑ in the correct box.

☐   **A**   Thank you for your recent application for the position of part-time waitress.

☐   **B**   pleased to be able to invite you to an interview at the restaurant on Tuesday 18th September at 3 p.m.

☐   **C**   Please arrive in good time and tell one of our friendly staff that you have come for an interview.

2   Circle the key word or phrase in the test-style question below.

> According to Text C1, list **two** reasons why Jen is the right person for this job.
>
> **(1 mark)**

3   Look carefully at Text C1 on page 54 and find the key word or phrase that you circled in the test-style question above. Circle or underline it.

> You might not find the correct answer in the same sentence as the key word or phrase. If this is the case, don't worry! Read the sentences before and after it, and look at any sub-headings to help you.

4   Read the sentence from Text C1 in which you found the key word or phrase. Answer the test-style question below.

> According to Text C1, what are **two** of the reasons why Jen is the right person for this position? Put a tick ☑ in the correct box.
>
> ☐   **A**   she used to work in a restaurant
> ☐   **B**   she likes cooking new recipes
> ☐   **C**   she is polite and hard-working
> ☐   **D**   she is energetic and organised
>
> **(1 mark)**

Using a dictionary

1   Imagine dividing a dictionary into four sections:

In which quarter of the dictionary would you find each of these words?
Circle the correct answer.

(a)   ululate   1st   2nd   3rd   4th

(b)   abduct   1st   2nd   3rd   4th

(c)   palatable   1st   2nd   3rd   4th

(d)   humerus   1st   2nd   3rd   4th

GUIDED   2   Use a dictionary to find the meanings of the words below. Draw lines to link each word with its correct meaning.

abduct   to take away illegally or kidnap

humerus   having a pleasant or acceptable taste

palatable   to howl or shout

ululate   a bone in the arm, extending from shoulder to elbow

3   Now, look at these sentences from Text A2 on page 51 and then answer the test-style question below.

> *Jules began designing clothes for her friends at the age of 16. Her exquisite designs are now sold around the world.*

Look up the word 'exquisite' in your dictionary and write down what it means.

....

....

(1 mark)

Choosing an answer

1   Which of these pieces of advice will help you when you are choosing the answer to a multiple choice question? Put a tick ☑ in the correct box.

     ☐   **A**   Read all the answers carefully before deciding which one is correct.

     ☐   **B**   If the answer is obvious, there is no need to read the text to check that it is correct.

     ☐   **C**   If you change your mind about the answer, put a tick in another box.

     ☐   **D**   If you don't know the answer, leave all the boxes blank.

2   Look at this student's answer to a multiple choice question.

> According to Text B1, what is the cost of a nine day trip to Barcelona, including coach travel, accommodation and activities? Put a tick ☑ in the correct box.
>
> ☐   **A**   £179
>
> ☑   **B**   £549
>
> ☑   **C**   £699
>
> ☐   **D**   £999
>
>   **(1 mark)**

Read Text B1 on page 52.

(a)   Has the student answered correctly?

....

....

(b)   Correct the student's answer to the multiple choice question above.

> Remember to check very carefully that
> you have selected the correct answer!

Writing your own answer

1   Look at the following statements about writing your own answer. Put a tick ☑ in the correct boxes.

> Make sure you give enough information to answer the question fully, but don't waste time writing more than is necessary!

	TRUE	FALSE
(a) You should read the question carefully to make sure you look for the correct information.	☐	☐
(b) You should always check your answer to make sure you have found the correct information.	☐	☐
(c) You need to be sure your answer is correct in questions like this, because you don't have four answers to choose from.	☐	☐
(d) You don't have to use complete sentences when you write your own answer.	☐	☐
(e) Your answer should fill the whole of the line you are given to write your answer on.	☐	☐

2   Look at three different students' responses to the same question below and Text B2 on page 53.

> According to Text B2, when does Ula's coach depart from Westerby? Write your answer on the line below.
>
> **(1 mark)**

Student A:
11.15 a.m.
on 18th April

Student B:
9.15 a.m.
on 17th April

Student C:
9.15 a.m.

(a)   Which student has given the best answer? Circle the answer you think is correct.

   A   B   C

(b)   Why is this the best answer?

....

....

Putting it into practice

Read Text A1 on page 50 and look at the questions below. Work through the steps that will help you to find the correct answer to the question. Put a tick next to each step as you complete it.

Step 1   Read the question. Make sure you know which text you need to look in to answer the question.   ☐ ☐

Step 2   Read the text and make sure you understand its main idea.   ☐ ☐

Step 3   Read the question again carefully. Make sure you know what it is asking you.   ☐ ☐

Step 4   Circle or underline the key word or phrase in the question.   ☐ ☐

Step 5   Search through the text to find the key word or phrase from the question. Circle or underline it.   ☐ ☐

Step 6   Read the sentence in the text in which you found the key word or phrase. Does it help you to answer the question? If not, read around the sentence to find the information you need.   ☐ ☐

Step 7   Answer the question.   ☐ ☐

---

1   According to Text A1, when will Westerby College be holding an Enterprise Day? Put a tick ☑ in the correct box.

☐   **A**   18th October

☐   **B**   4th March

☐   **C**   9th January

☐   **D**   6th August

(1 mark)

---

2   According to Text A1, what is the title of the talk in which Nish Patel will show you how to think positively about your future? Put a tick ☑ in the correct box.

☐   **A**   writing application forms

☐   **B**   how I set up my own business

☐   **C**   get ready for success

☐   **D**   what employers want

(1 mark)

9

Headings and sub-headings

1   Look at the headings of the texts below. What can you find out about each text from its heading? Write **one or more** ideas on the answer lines provided.

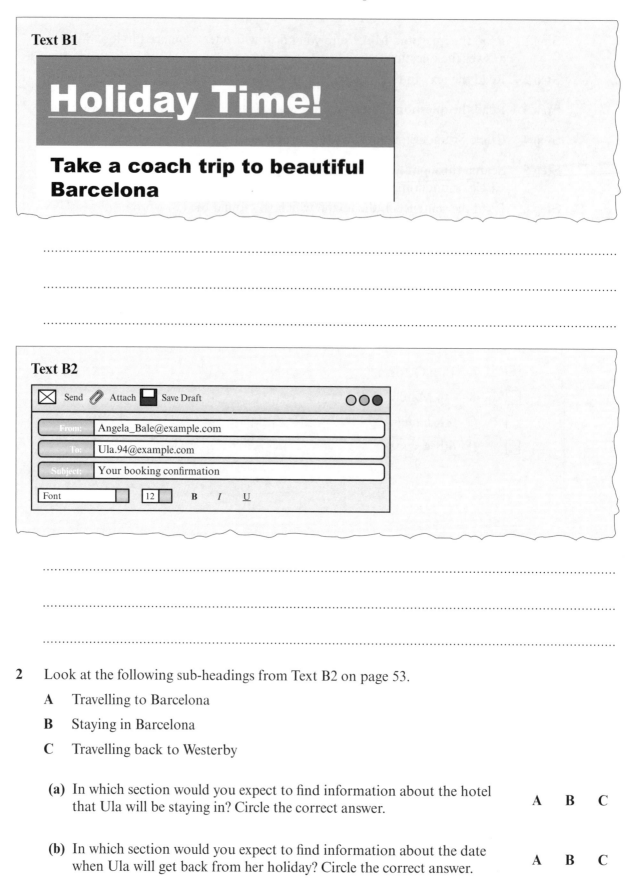

Text B1

Holiday Time!

Take a coach trip to beautiful Barcelona

....

....

....

Text B2

☒ Send   ✏ Attach   ▣ Save Draft   ○○●

From: Angela_Bale@example.com

To: Ula.94@example.com

Subject: Your booking confirmation

Font   12   **B**   *I*   U̲

....

....

....

2   Look at the following sub-headings from Text B2 on page 53.

A   Travelling to Barcelona

B   Staying in Barcelona

C   Travelling back to Westerby

(a) In which section would you expect to find information about the hotel that Ula will be staying in? Circle the correct answer.   A   B   C

(b) In which section would you expect to find information about the date when Ula will get back from her holiday? Circle the correct answer.   A   B   C

Paragraphs and bullet points

1   Look at these three paragraphs from Text C2.

> In the test, try to summarise each paragraph of a text in your head as you read. This will help you to understand the text and correctly answer the questions.

1	Thank you for your recent application for the position of part-time waitress. I am pleased to be able to invite you to an interview at the restaurant on Tuesday 18th September at 3 p.m. Please arrive in good time and tell one of our friendly staff that you have come for an interview.
2	You will be interviewed by: • Helen Baxter, the restaurant owner • Amy Stubbs, the restaurant manager The interview will last approximately 20 minutes.
3	Please confirm you are able to attend the interview by ringing us on the above number or by emailing us at amy@biteswesterby.co.uk

Now look at these summaries of the paragraphs. Which summary goes with which paragraph? Circle each correct answer.

(a)   who will conduct the interview and how long it will last   **1**   **2**   **3**

(b)   when and where the interview is   **1**   **2**   **3**

(c)   how to confirm you will attend the interview   **1**   **2**   **3**

2   How do bullet points make a text easier to read?

....

....

3   Look carefully at the bullet points in paragraph 2 to answer the test-style question below.

> What is the name of the restaurant owner? Put a tick ☑ in the correct box.
>
> ☐   **A**   Ms J Roberts
>
> ☐   **B**   Bites Restaurant
>
> ☐   **C**   Helen Baxter
>
> ☐   **D**   Amy Stubbs
>
>   **(1 mark)**

Tables and timetables

1   Look at this extract from Text A1, which lists details of talks and workshops at a local college's Enterprise Day.

Text A1

Timetable of events

Talks and workshops	Details	Times
What employers want	Barry Chum of Westerby Business Forum explains what employers are looking for when they recruit staff.	Start: 9.00 a.m. Finish: 9.45 a.m.

Answer the three questions below by circling each correct answer.

(a) In which column will you find information about the name of the talk or workshop?   Talks and workshops   Details   Times

(b) Which column tells you when each talk or workshop will start and finish?   Talks and workshops   Details   Times

(c) In which column will you find information describing what the talk or workshop will be about?   Talks and workshops   Details   Times

2   (a) Now look at the whole of Text A1 on page 50 and complete the questions below. When will Mary Porter's talk 'Succeeding in interviews' begin? Put a tick ☑ in the correct box.

☐ A   9.00 a.m.

☐ B   10.00 a.m.

☐ C   11.30 a.m.

☐ D   1.15 p.m.

(b) Ali is free between 12.30 p.m. and 2.30 p.m. on Friday 4th March. According to Text A1, which is the only talk or workshop he will be able to attend? Put a tick ☑ in the correct box.

☐ A   Succeeding in interviews

☐ B   Writing application forms

☐ C   Setting up your own business

☐ D   How I set up my own business

Forms

Look at Text C1 on page 54. Jen has filled in an application form for a job at a local restaurant.

According to text C1, which post is Jen applying for? Put a tick ☑ in the correct box.

☐ **A** part-time waitress

☐ **B** chef

☐ **C** admin support

☐ **D** kitchen porter

(1 mark)

1 In which section of the form could you find the correct answer? Circle the correct answer.

Name   **Post applied for**   **Address**

Previous relevant experience   **Which days are you available for work?**

2 Read the section you identified in question 1 and choose the correct answer from the options above.

3 In which section of the form might you find information about other jobs that Jen has had in the past? Circle the correct answer.

Name   **Post applied for**   **Address**

Previous relevant experience   **Which days are you available for work?**

4 Which two sections of the form has Jen forgotten to fill in? Write **two** answers on the lines below.

....

....

....

Putting it into practice

Read Text A2 on page 51, and answer questions 1 to 4.

1 Jamie wants to read all about how Jules Jardine started her own business.

According to Text A2, which chapter of her book should he read? Put a tick ☑ in the correct box.

☐ **A** Chapter Two

☐ **B** Chapter Four

☐ **C** Chapter Six

☐ **D** Chapter Eight   **(1 mark)**

> Remember to:
> - read the question carefully
> - highlight a key word or phrase in the question
> - read the text carefully, looking for the key word or phrase from the question
> - use the information you find to answer the question.

2 According to Text A2, on which pages of Jules Jardine's book can you read about her first job? Put a tick ☑ in the correct box.

☐ **A** pages 1–14

☐ **B** pages 15–27

☐ **C** pages 28–41

☐ **D** pages 42–49   **(1 mark)**

3 According to Text A2, Jules Jardine is a judge on a television series. What is the name of the television series?

....

....

                                                                                (1 mark)

4 According to Text A2, when was Jules Jardine's book first published?

....

....

                                                                                (1 mark)

Your writing test

1   Read these statements about the writing test. Put a tick ☑ in the correct boxes.

		TRUE	FALSE
(a)	You will be asked to complete two writing tasks.	☐	☐
(b)	You will be asked to plan, draft and write a final response for both writing tasks.	☐	☐
(c)	You only need to plan one of the writing tasks. You can make up the other one as you write it.	☐	☐
(d)	All of the writing tasks are worth the same number of marks.	☐	☐
(e)	You will be given 45 minutes in total to complete the writing test.	☐	☐

2   Look at the statements that you think are false. Write a sentence for each, correcting the false information and giving accurate information about the writing test.

....

....

....

....

3   Which of these different types of text could you be asked to write in the writing test?
Put a tick ☑ in the correct boxes.

☐ **A**   an email

☐ **B**   a letter

☐ **C**   instructions

☐ **D**   a story

☐ **E**   a report

☐ **F**   a notice or advert

☐ **G**   a poem

☐ **H**   a personal statement

Reading the question

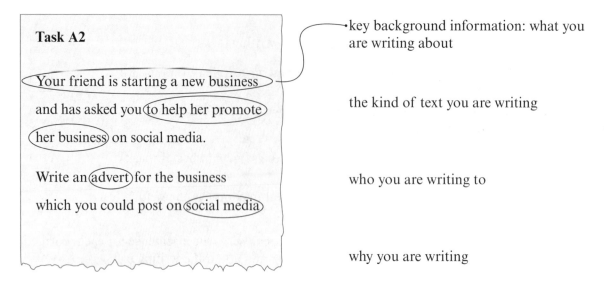

GUIDED 1 Look at an extract from Task A2 below. Draw lines linking the notes to the circled key words and phrases in the task.

Task A2

Your friend is starting a new business and has asked you to help her promote her business on social media.

Write an advert for the business which you could post on social media.

key background information: what you are writing about

the kind of text you are writing

who you are writing to

why you are writing

2 Look at the extract from Task C1 below.

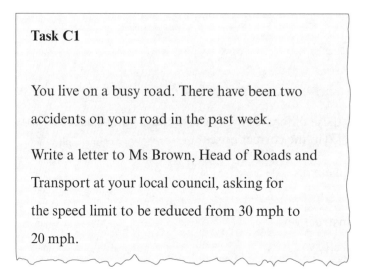

Task C1

You live on a busy road. There have been two accidents on your road in the past week.

Write a letter to Ms Brown, Head of Roads and Transport at your local council, asking for the speed limit to be reduced from 30 mph to 20 mph.

(a) Circle all the key words and phrases in the task.

(b) Write your own notes around the task to make sure you have identified:
   • what you are writing about
   • the kind of text you are writing
   • who you are writing to
   • why you are writing.

3 Choose at least one other writing task from pages 56–61. Find all the key words and phrases in your chosen task. Label them to make sure you understand what the task is asking you to do.

Reasons for writing

1 Look at these extracts from two writing tasks.

> **Task A2**
>
> Your friend is starting a new business and has asked you to help her promote it on social media. Write an advert for the business which you could post on social media.

> **Task B2**
>
> A friend has sent you an email inviting you to go on holiday with them. You are not free on the dates your friend has booked the holiday, so you will not be able to go. Write an email to tell your friend.

What is the reason for writing each of the writing tasks above? Complete these sentences.

(a) The reason for writing Task A2 is to .... and

.... the reader.

(b) The reason for writing Task B2 is to .... and

.... the reader.

2 What do you want the reader to think when they have read your responses to the two tasks above? Write at least **one** sentence in each of the thought bubbles below.

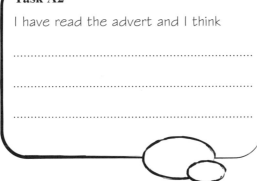

Task A2

I have read the advert and I think

....

....

....

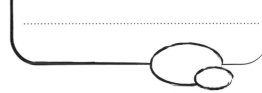

Task B2

I have read the email and I think

....

....

....

3 Now, look at Task A1 on page 56. Write **two** sentences identifying the reason for writing and what you would want the reader to think when they have read it.

....

....

....

Who you are writing to

1 Look at the extract from a writing task below.

> **Task B1**
>
> Your school/college/workplace is organising a Party Night to raise money for a local charity.
> You have offered to arrange the food for 50 guests to eat at the Party Night.
> Write a letter to a local supermarket, asking if they will donate some food to help feed
> your guests.

Look at these ideas that one student wrote in their plan for this task. Which of their ideas would you include in your response to the task? Put a tick ☑ in the correct boxes.

☐ **A** information about my college and my catering course

☐ **B** we are having a party night at the Community Centre on 14th June

☐ **C** when the Party Night starts and finishes

☐ **D** we need enough food for 50 guests

☐ **E** we need buffet food like sandwiches and crisps

☐ **F** information about the DJ who will do the music at the party

☐ **G** information about the charity we are raising money for

☐ **H** how much money we want to raise for the charity

2 Now, look at Task B2 on page 59. Use the space below to write down some ideas you could include in your response.

....

....

....

....

....

....

....

....

3 Look at your ideas for question 2 again. Does your reader need to know everything you have written down? Cross out any ideas you do not need to include.

Planning

1   Thinking about the bullet points in each writing task will help you to plan your writing. Look at Task C1 on page 60. Note down at least **one** idea for each of the bullet points in the task.

> Remember: when you plan, think about **who** you are writing to and **why** you are writing.

• details of the accidents that have happened in the past week	
• why you think that slowing down the traffic will make your road a safer place to live	
• any other benefits of reducing the speed limit	

2   Asking yourself some key questions can help you to plan your writing tasks.

Look at the bullet points above again and the notes you have already made.

Ask yourself the key questions below. Answer them using your ideas.

(a) **What** accidents have happened? ....

(b) **Where** have they happened? ....

(c) **When** did they happen? ....

(d) **Why** would slowing down the traffic help the problem? ....

(e) **How** could the traffic be slowed down? ....

3   What key questions could you ask yourself to help you plan an answer to Task A1 on page 56? Write some key questions below.

(a) **What** ....?

(b) **Where** ....?

(c) **When** ....?

(d) **Why** ....?

(e) **How** ....?

Organising

1. Look at one student's plan for Task B2 on page 59. They have numbered three of the ideas on their plan. Number the rest of the ideas, putting them in a logical order.

① Thanks for the invite.

I can't go in June.

My dad's paying me to paint his house in June.

I promised him and I can't let him down.

② I wish I could come.

I need the money!

Ant said he wanted to go on a sunny holiday.

③ I bet you'll have a great time. I'm jealous!

2. Look at Task A1 on page 56.

    (a) Use the space below to note down all the ideas you could use in your response to the task. Remember to:

    - use the bullet points in the task to help you
    - ask yourself some key questions to help you come up with even more ideas
    - check you have covered all the bullet points in your plan.

....

....

....

....

....

....

....

....

    (b) Number all your ideas, putting them in a logical order.

Remember to check your plan carefully and change it if you need to.

Drafting

The draft you produce in your test will be marked. The mark will go towards your final mark for the whole test.

1   Look at the statements below. They are about the advantages of drafting before you write your final answer. How strongly do you agree with each one? Number them 1–4 where:

> Remember: you can write your plan as notes, but you should **always** write your draft in complete sentences. It will help you see how you can improve your writing when you write your final answer.

   • 1 is the one you agree with most strongly
   • 4 is the one you agree with least strongly.

   Your draft is a good opportunity to:

   ☐   check you are happy with the ideas in your writing

   ☐   check you are happy with the order of ideas in your writing

   ☐   organise your writing in paragraphs

   ☐   add detail to your writing

2   Complete the sentences below. They are about ways in which you can make changes to your draft.

When you draft your writing you can divide a paragraph into two paragraphs. To show where you want a new paragraph to start, you can use this mark: ....

.There are two ways to add an extra word or sentence to your writing. If you are just adding a word or two you can write it above the line and use this mark to show where it goes: .... If you want to add a whole sentence, it is clearer to write the extra sentence at the bottom of your draft. Use an arrow or an asterisk, which looks like this ...., to show where the extra sentence should go.

Checking

1   Look at this list of common writing mistakes.

- there / their / they're
- too / to / two
- missing full stops
- missing capital letters
- missing apostrophes
- missing out a word

How many of these mistakes can you find in this student's writing? Circle and correct them.

> Hi jem
>
> I wont be able to come to tenerife with you next month because im going to be to busy working.
>
> its really annoying and i'm gutted but their are loads people who would like to go you should ask adam and baz because I don't think their busy i bet they'd love it.
>
> all the best,
>
> Dai

2   Now, look at a piece of **your** writing.

Which of the common mistakes above have you made in your writing?

Make a list of the mistakes you make most often in the table below.

Spellings	Capital letters and full stops	Making sense

Had a go ☐   Nearly there ☐   Nailed it! ☐

Putting it into practice

Write a plan and a draft for Task B2 on page 59.

Write a plan and a draft for Task B2 on page 59.

Remember to check your writing very carefully when you have finished. Use the list you made on page 22 of common mistakes in your writing to check you haven't repeated them in your draft!

....

....

....

....

....

....

....

....

....

....

....

....

....

....

....

....

....

....

....

....

....

....

Writing an email

1   Look at Task C2 on page 61 and the three different responses below.

Are the responses too formal, too informal or just right? Put a tick ☑ in the correct box.

> Dear Maz
>
> I am very pleased to hear that you are considering moving to this area. It is a very pleasant place to live with many things to do and several employment opportunities. I very much look forward to hearing your decision.
>
> Yours sincerely
> Dan

☐ Too formal   ☐ Too informal   ☐ Just right

> Hi Maz
>
> Great news! I reckon you should definitely move here cos it's a great place to live and there's loads of work and loads to do. I love it here. Bet you would too.
>
> See ya
> Dan

☐ Too formal   ☐ Too informal   ☐ Just right

> Hi Maz
>
> It was good to hear that you're thinking of moving here. I really like living here. You should have no trouble getting work and there's a really good choice of things to do in the evenings and at weekends. Let me know what you decide!
>
> All the best
> Dan

☐ Too formal   ☐ Too informal   ☐ Just right

2   Choose one of the emails above and rewrite it.
Make it more appropriate for the reader.

....

....

....

....

....

....

Had a go ☐   Nearly there ☐   Nailed it! ☐

Writing a letter

Look at Task C1 on page 60 and one student's response to it below.

---

17 Entwistle Avenue
Estrick
EL1 5Q3

78 Salisbury Grove
Estrick
EL1 8BW

A

Dear Sir or Madam / Miss Brown / Mrs Brown / Ms Brown

I'm writing to ask you to drop the speed limit on my road to 20 mph. There's been two accidents on my road in the past week. People got hurt and one was a seven year old kid.

People drive down our road much too quick. This is what causes accidents and it makes our road dangerous and noisy. I think you should definitely make the speed limit lower.

Yours Sincerely / sincerely / Faithfully / faithfully
Becca

---

1   What should be written in box A?

    ....

2   Look at the words in boxes in the greeting and the sign-off. Which **one** of the four choices for each is correct? Cross out the **three** that are incorrect.

3   Some of the language in the letter is too informal. Cross out any informal language and write a suitable alternative above to make it more appropriate.

Writing instructions

1   You need to give your reader enough detail to carry out the instructions easily. Look at one student's instructions on using a hammer.

> Hit a nail with it and the nail will go in.

What other details would make these instructions more helpful to the reader? You could think about telling your reader:

- how to hold the hammer
- how to hold the nail
- how to hit the nail
- how to be careful.

Rewrite the instructions on the lines below, making them more detailed and easy to follow.

....

....

....

....

GUIDED   2   Look at the instructions below. Replace the numbers with words from the box below to show the order in which you complete the steps.

> **Words that indicate time**
>
> First, ...   Then, ...   Next, ...
>
> After that, ...   Finally, ...

How to take a tablet

1. First, pour yourself a glass of water.

2. .... remove the tablet from its packaging.

3. .... place the tablet at the back of your tongue.

4. .... take a large sip of water, tipping your head back as you swallow it.

Writing a report

Look at the test-style task below.

> Your school/college/workplace wants to hold an event to raise money for a local charity. You
> have been asked to write a report, suggesting different kinds of event you could hold to raise
> money – and how popular you think they would be.
>
> In your report, you could:
>
> - suggest two or three different ideas for events to raise money
> - explain which event you think would be most popular and why
> - suggest how that event could be organised.

1 Write the first **one or two** sentences of a report, explaining to the reader what your report is
   about and why you are writing it.

   ....

   ....

   ....

   ....

2 Write down **three** sub-headings that you could use to
   organise your ideas.

   > Remember, the best sub-headings
   > are short and snappy!

   (a) ....

   ....

   ....

   (b) ....

   ....

   ....

   (c) ....

   ....

   ....

3 What could you write about under each of the sub-headings you wrote in question 2? Write
   down at least **one** idea next to each sub-heading.

Writing a notice or advert

1 What is the key purpose of a notice or advert? Put a tick ☑ in the correct box.

☐ **A** to give the reader some information about an item for sale or an event taking place

☐ **B** to give the reader a very detailed description of the item or event

☐ **C** to give the reader a very detailed explanation of how the item works or how the event will be organised

☐ **D** to give the reader advice about how to use an item

2 What should you include in a notice? Complete the sentences below.

You need to give your notice or advert a .... to grab the

reader's attention and make them want to read the rest of it. You should give them some

.... about the item or event you are advertising, but not

too much. You should also include .... so the reader knows

where they can get more information if they need to.

GUIDED **3** When you are deciding what information the reader would want to know, it can be helpful to note down some questions the reader might want answered.

Look at Task A2 on page 57, then think about the questions a reader might want to ask about your friend's business. Complete the questions below.

What product or service is this business offering?

Why should I use this product or service?

Where .... ?

How .... ?

When .... ?

Writing a personal statement

1　Which of these questions should you focus on answering in your personal statement?
Put a tick ☑ in the correct box.

☐　**A**　Why might I not be the right person for the job?

☐　**B**　Why am I the right person for the job?

☐　**C**　How much money will I earn?

☐　**D**　Will I get paid holidays?

2　Imagine that you see an advert for your dream job, working for your dream company.

Write down **four** ideas explaining why you want to apply for the job.

....

....

....

....

Why am I interested?

....

....

....

....

>GUIDED>　3　A personal statement is a formal text. Write down
four features of writing that you must remember to use in
a formal text.

> Think about your interests and how the job and company relate to them.

(a)　Paragraphs

(b)　..

(c)　..

(d)　..

Putting it into practice

Write a list of the key features of each type of text in the boxes below.

Remember to think about:

- **Format:** Do you need to include addresses, dates, greetings, sign-offs, sub-headings, other format features?

- **Formality:** Is it a formal or an informal text? Should you use formal language or more informal language?

- **Ideas:** What can you use to help you think of and plan ideas for each kind of text?

Emails	Letters
....	....
....	....
....	....
....	....
....	....

Instructions	Reports
....	....
....	....
....	....
....	....
....	....

Notices or adverts	Personal statements
....	....
....	....
....	....
....	....

Paragraphs

1   Look at these statements about paragraphs. Which are true and which are false?
    Put a tick ☑ in the correct boxes.

		TRUE	FALSE
(a)	A paragraph should be at least five sentences long.	☐	☐
(b)	You should start a new paragraph when you write about a different aspect of your topic.	☐	☐
(c)	You should indent the first line of each paragraph when writing by hand.	☐	☐
(d)	You should leave a line after each paragraph when writing by hand.	☐	☐
(e)	You should leave a line between each paragraph when typing on a computer.	☐	☐

2   Look at this student's plan for Task B1 on page 58.

Dear...

organising a Party Night at Westerby College – 18th Sept at 8 p.m.

to raise money for the new Day Centre for elderly people

the Day Centre will help them get out the house and meet new people

it will be fun

hoping to raise £1000

there will be music, dancing, food

would be very grateful if you could donate some food, for example, sausage rolls, soft drinks etc

needs to feed 50 people

Yours faithfully...

(a)   How many paragraphs should there be in this student's letter? Put a tick ☑ in
      the correct box.

      ☐ **A** one

      ☐ **B** two

      ☐ **C** three

      ☐ **D** four

(b)   Write **one or two** sentences on the lines below, explaining your answer to question 2(a).

....

....

....

....

Sentences

1   Which of the following options are sentences? Put a tick ☑ in the correct boxes.

    ☐ **A** I did work experience at my local beauty salon for two weeks.

    ☐ **B** Which was great.

    ☐ **C** I learned a lot about dealing with customers and helping the owner do the treatments.

    ☐ **D** I loved it.

    ☐ **E** Really fun going to the cinema.

2   Each of the examples below contains **at least two** sentences. Correct each one by adding a capital letter at the start of each sentence and a full stop at the end of each sentence.

(a) we are organising a party night at Westerby College on 18th September we are going to be raising money for the new Day Centre for elderly people

(b) the Day Centre will help old people to get out of the house and make new friends it's a really worthwhile cause we're hoping to raise over a thousand pounds

(c) we would like you to donate food to help the party and help the elderly people of Westerby we would be very grateful and so would they

3   Look at this student's response to Task A2. Use **one or more** of the words in the box below to fill each gap and make the sentences more interesting and detailed.

large   tasty   always   affordable
huge   yummy   very   extremely

Do you enjoy .... desserts?

Delicious desserts has a .... selection

of .... sweet treats just for you.

We .... use locally sourced ingredients. Next time you're

in Estrick Town Centre, come and try our .... delicious

desserts!

Talking about the present

1 Look at these sentences from a student's response to Task C1 on page 60. Each sentence describes the situation at the moment. Circle the correct verb in each sentence, making sure each verb is in the present tense.

(a) I <u>am / was</u> writing because I <u>think / thought</u> the speed limit should be reduced.

(b) Every day, cars <u>speed / sped</u> up and down our road.

(c) Some of them <u>travel / travelled</u> at more than 40 mph.

(d) I <u>worry / worried</u> about this because I <u>think / thought</u> it <u>is / was</u> dangerous for the people who <u>live / lived</u> on my road.

(e) Old people and children <u>are / were</u> the most likely to be hurt if we <u>do / did</u> not do something about this.

(f) I hope you <u>are / were</u> able to do something about this.

GUIDED **2** Look at the sentences below. Circle the verb in each sentence.

(a) My home town (was) a great place.

(b) There was a great choice of shops.

(c) It had a cinema and a sports centre.

(d) The people were very friendly.

(e) I loved it.

GUIDED **3** The sentences in question 2 are all in the past tense. Rewrite the sentences in the present tense by changing the verbs.

(a) My home town is a great place.

(b) ....

(c) ....

(d) ....

(e) ....

Making the verb match

1   Look at the sentences below. Circle the verb in each sentence. Underline the subject of each verb.

   (a)   I got your email yesterday.

   (b)   Your email was very surprising.

   (c)   Nobody knew that.

2   You will almost certainly use the verb 'to be' in the writing test. Test your knowledge of this verb by completing the sentences below using 'am', 'is' or 'are'.

> Look closely at the subject of the verb in each sentence.

   (a)   There .... seven people in my house.

   (b)   I .... the youngest.

   (c)   My grandmother .... the oldest.

   (d)   My brother .... the most annoying.

   (e)   We .... a very close family.

3   Look at the sentences below, taken from a student's response to Task A1. Circle the correct verb in each sentence.

   (a)   My friends and I is / are very active.

   (b)   We has / have lots of skills we can use to help us survive on a desert island.

   (c)   I build / builds things all the time using old bits of wood and scrap metal.

   (d)   One of us is / are a chef so we will not be hungry.

   (e)   We get / gets along really well and we never argue / argues.

> Make sure you have chosen the correct form to match the subject of the verb.

Talking about the past

1   Circle the correct verb in each of the sentences below, making sure they are:

* the correct past tense
* spelled correctly.

    (a) I writed / wrote you an email last week.

    (b) I tryed / tried to call but no one answerd / answered.

    (c) I slammed / slamed the phone down.

    (d) The phone rang / ringed and I hurryed / hurried to get it.

    (e) I hopped / hoped you would be in touch.

⟩**GUIDED**⟩   2   Write the correct past tense of the verb 'to be' to complete the sentences below.

    (a) My first job was working in a pet shop.

    (b) My parents .... really pleased I had found a job.

    (c) We .... all really pleased.

    (d) You .... lucky to find any job where we lived.

    (e) So I .... really lucky to find a job that I loved.

3   Some other verbs have an unusual past tense. The sentences below are all in the present tense. Identify the verb in each sentence. Then, rewrite the sentence using the past tense form of the verb.

    (a) I go to college one day a week.   ....

    (b) I bring my own lunch to college.   ....

    (c) I take sandwiches and a drink.   ....

Talking about the future

 1 Each sentence below is written in the present tense. Rewrite each sentence twice, once using the verb 'will' and once using the verb 'going to'.

(a) I start a new part-time job in October.

> I will start a new part-time job in October.

> I am going to start a new part-time job in October.

(b) I work Saturdays and Sundays.

....

....

(c) I am a postman delivering parcels to people's houses.

....

....

> You can write about the future in two ways. You can use the verb 'will' or the verb 'going to'.

 2 Read the sentences below that have been written in the future tense. Rewrite them using the words 'about to' to show that they are going to happen in the immediate future.

(a) I will leave my job.

> I am about to leave my job.

(b) I will start looking for a new job.

....

(c) I will start my own business.

....

Using joining words

1   The sentences below are taken from a student's response to Task A1. Choose **one** joining word from the list on the below to link each pair of sentences. Try to use each joining word at least once.

> **Joining words**
>
> and | but | or

(a) We love camping. .... We go every year.

(b) We go for a week. .... Sometimes we go for a fortnight.

(c) We spend all our time together. .... We never argue.

(d) Viewers would enjoy our banter. .... They would watch the programme every week.

> Remember to make any changes to full stops or capital letters that are needed once the sentences are linked.

2   Use the questions and suggested words in the boxes to help you think of details you could add to each sentence.

When?	Why?	Always?
when | until | as soon as	because | so | as	if | but | although

(a) We love camping ....

....

(b) We go for a week ....

....

(c) We spend all our time together ....

....

(d) Viewers would enjoy our banter ....

....

Putting it into practice

Plan and write your response to Task C2 on page 61.

> Remember to:
> • write in paragraphs
> • write in complete sentences using accurate punctuation
> • choose the correct verb forms when you are talking about the past, present and future
> • use joining words to link or add detail to some of your ideas.

Plan and write your response to Task C2 on page 61.

Capital letters

Look at this extract from a letter:

> 17 snow hill
> westerby
> po19 4hh
>
> 4th november 2016
>
> dear gramps
>
> i've just watched that old james bond film you said was really good called goldfinger.
> it was pretty good.

GUIDED **1** Write down **five** places where you should use a capital letter.

    (a) At the start of a sentence.

    (b) ....

    (c) ....

    (d) ....

    (e) ....

2 **(a)** Circle all the places in the letter above where the writer should have used a capital letter.

    (b) Correct the writer's mistakes, adding capital letters where necessary.

3 Write **three** sentences. Write one about where you live, one about a person you know, and one about somewhere you have been on holiday. Make sure you use capital letters correctly.

> Follow the rules you wrote in question 1.

....

....

....

....

....

....

Ending a sentence

1   Look at the sentences below from one student's response to Task C2 on page 61. Which ones are punctuated correctly? Put a tick ☑ in the correct boxes.

> Remember: you can link two ideas with a joining word. You can separate two ideas with a full stop. You **cannot** separate two ideas with a comma.

   (a) Thanks for your email, I haven't heard from you in ages. ☐

   (b) I think you should definitely move here, it's a great place to live. ☐

   (c) There are some nice places to live and lots of places to go out. ☐

   (d) There are some great flats but some are quite expensive. ☐

   (e) I wish you would move here because it would be great to see you more often. ☐

2   Some of the sentences below are questions. Correct the punctuation by putting a tick ☑ in the correct boxes.

	Question mark	Full stop
(a) When did you decide to move	☐	☐
(b) Have you got a moving date yet	☐	☐
(c) You should easily get work round here	☐	☐
(d) We could get a flat together	☐	☐
(e) How does that sound	☐	☐

3   Now, look closely at the punctuation in the sentences below. Circle and correct **all** the mistakes. Look out for:
- commas that should be full stops
- missing full stops
- missing question marks.

> I've lived here all my life, I've never wanted to move away because it's where all my friends and family are. It's got great places to go out, great shops and great places to eat out who wouldn't want to live in a place like this

Putting it into practice

Use the answer lines below to plan your response to Task B1 on page 58.

> Check every sentence in your writing very carefully **two times**, looking out for:
> - missing capital letters
> - missing or incorrect full stops.

....

....

....

....

....

....

....

....

....

Now, write the first **five** sentences of your response:

....

....

....

....

....

....

....

....

....

....

....

Spelling tips

> Remember these useful tips to help you spell correctly in the test.
> - Very few words end in -**ley**.
> - It's worth learning the most common words that contain silent letters.
> - Learn words that contain double letters by 'sounding the syllables', for example **ad-dress**.

1   There is a silent letter missing from each of these words. Spell the word correctly on the line below.

   (a) wen   **(b)** thum   **(c)** coud   **(d)** nee   **(e)** shoud

   ....

   (f) rong   **(g)** wy   **(h)** nock   **(i)** wat   **(j)** dout

   ....

2   Which of these pairs of words is spelled correctly? Circle the correct spelling for each pair.

   (a) valley / vally   **(b)** suddenley / suddenly   **(c)** definitely / definitley

   (d) sincerely / sincerley   **(e)** completely / completley   **(f)** ugly / ugley

   (g) nearley / nearly   **(h)** likely / likley   **(i)** lonely / lonley

3   **One** letter should be doubled in each of these words. Spell the word correctly on the line below.

   (a) disapoint   **(b)** disapear   **(c)** dificult   **(d)** necesary   **(e)** tomorow

   ....

   (f) diferent   **(g)** posible   **(h)** sucess   **(i)** imediate   **(j)** begining

   ....

4   Make a list of any spellings on this page that you do not feel confident about. Learn them using the look–say–cover–write–check method.

   ....

   ....

   ....

   ....

Plurals

1   Identify the correct spelling of the plurals below. Put a tick ☑ in the correct boxes.

   (a) lunchs   ☐   lunches   ☐

   (b) wishs   ☐   wishes   ☐

   (c) countries   ☐   countrys   ☐

   (d) families   ☐   familys   ☐

   (e) days   ☐   daies   ☐

   (f) boys   ☐   boies   ☐

2   Look carefully at the plurals above. What are the rules for creating these kinds of plurals?
     Complete the sentences below.

   (a)   If a word ends in **'ch', 'sh', 'x', 's' or 'ss'**, you make it plural by ....

     ....

   (b)   If a word ends in a consonant (any letter that is not a vowel) and then a 'y', you make it

       plural by ....

     ....

   (c)   If a word ends in a vowel (a, e, i, o or u) and then a 'y', you make it plural by

     ....

     ....

3   Write the correct plural underneath each of the words below.

   (a) body   **(b)** baby

   ....

   (c) way   **(d)** journey

   ....

   (e) glass   **(f)** fish

   ....

Prefixes

> **GUIDED** 1   A prefix can often be used to turn a word into its opposite.
>
> Which prefixes turn the root words below into their opposites?

> When 'all' is used as a prefix, it drops an 'l', making the prefix 'al-'.

(a)   Draw a line linking each root word to the prefix that turns it into its opposite.

(b)   Write the opposite of each root word in the box next to it.

Prefix	Root word	Opposite
A dis	1 helpful	unhelpful
B im	2 like	....
C in	3 understand	....
D mis	4 correct	....
E un	5 mature	....

2   All the words below are made up of a prefix and a root word. Identify the correct spellings by putting a tick ☑ in the correct boxes.

(a) dis + appear =   disappear ☐   dissapear ☐

(b) un + necessary =   unnecessary ☐   unecessary ☐

(c) mis + spell =   mispell ☐   misspell ☐

(d) all + ways =   always ☐   allways ☐

(e) dis + appoint =   dissappoint ☐   disappoint ☐

(f) all + together =   alltogether ☐   altogether ☐

(g) mis + take =   mistake ☐   misstake ☐

(h) dis + satisfied =   dissatisfied ☐   disatisfied ☐

Suffixes

1   Some root words do not change their spelling when you add a suffix. Look at the suffixes below.

-ed   -er   -ing   -est   -ness   -able   -ment

How many new words can you make by adding these suffixes to the three root words below?

Write as many as you can in the table. Then check your spelling.

(a) cook	(b) enjoy	(c) slow

2   Some root words change their spelling when you add a suffix.

Identify the correct spelling of the root words + suffixes below. Put a tick ☑ in the correct boxes.

(a) stopping   ☐   stoping   ☐

(b) begged   ☐   beged   ☐

(c) happyer   ☐   happier   ☐

(d) heavyest   ☐   heaviest   ☐

(e) haveing   ☐   having   ☐

(f) makeing   ☐   making   ☐

3   Complete the spelling rules for suffixes below.

(a) When you add a suffix to **most** shorter root words that end with a single consonant,

....

....

(b) When you add **most** suffixes to a root word whose last two letters are a consonant then a 'y',

....

....

(c) When you add a suffix that begins with a vowel to a word ending in 'e', ...

....

....

Tricky spellings 1

1   All of these tricky spellings appear in the sentences below.

Find and circle **all** of the tricky spellings.

> their / there / they're
>
> we're / were / wear / where
>
> of / off

Where I work, all of us have to wear overalls. They're comfortable and keep paint off our clothes. We're in trouble if we don't. There are some new supervisors there who keep their eyes on us all the time. The old supervisors were much nicer.

>**GUIDED** 2   Use the sentences above to remind you of the meaning of each tricky spelling. Then write your own definition of each one to help you remember it.

(a)   their *belonging to them*

(b)   there ....

....

(c)   they're ....

....

(d)   we're ....

....

(e)   were ....

....

(f)   wear ....

....

(g)   where ....

....

(h)   of ....

....

(i)   off ....

....

Tricky spellings 2

1   **Three** words are missing from the sentences below: to / too / two
Write the correctly spelled word in each space.

(a)   There are .... different countries I am interested in.

(b)   I am interested in going .... America and I would like to visit France

....

2   **Two** words are missing from the sentence below: our / are

Write the correctly spelled word in each space.

Both of .... dogs .... house trained.

3   **Three** words are missing from the sentence below: no / know / now

Write the correctly spelled word in each space.

(a)   I don't .... any good plumbers in this town.

(b)   There used to be lots of them, but there are .... good plumbers

....

4   **Two** words are missing from the sentence below: bought / brought

Write the correctly spelled word in each space.

(a)   I .... some crisps at the supermarket.

(b)   I .... them home and ate them.

Tricky spellings 3

Each row of the table below shows three different versions of a tricky spelling.

Only one of the spellings on each row is correct. Put a tick ☑ in the correct boxes.

1	thought	☐	thougt	☐	thout	☐
2	straigt	☐	straght	☐	straight	☐
3	sight	☐	sigt	☐	siht	☐
4	diffacult	☐	difficult	☐	dificult	☐
5	dissapear	☐	disappear	☐	dissappear	☐
6	begining	☐	beggining	☐	beginning	☐
7	definite	☐	defenite	☐	definate	☐
8	separate	☐	seperate	☐	seprate	☐
9	diferent	☐	different	☐	diffrent	☐
10	becuase	☐	becuse	☐	because	☐
11	peeple	☐	poeple	☐	people	☐
12	rember	☐	remember	☐	rememeber	☐
13	believe	☐	beleive	☐	belive	☐
14	friend	☐	frend	☐	freind	☐
15	peice	☐	pece	☐	piece	☐
16	busness	☐	business	☐	buisness	☐
17	deside	☐	decide	☐	deceide	☐
18	decision	☐	desision	☐	desicion	☐

Check your answers on page 72. Use the space below to practise any spellings you are not sure about.

Putting it into practice

Plan your response to Task C1 on page 60 in the space below.

....

....

....

....

....

....

Now write your response to Task C1 on page 60 in the space below.

....

....

....

....

....

....

....

....

....

....

....

Check your spelling carefully and make a list of any words you have misspelled. Learn your list by heart so that you can:

- spell these words correctly in the writing test
- look out for them when you are checking the spelling in the writing test.

TEXT A1

Jamie sees a notice in his local newspaper.

Westerby College Enterprise Day

Come and join us at Westerby College on Friday 4th March for an Enterprise Day. Get some help and information about how to find work and how to start your own business.

Timetable of events

Talks and workshops	Details	Times
What employers want	Barry Chum of Westerby Business Forum explains what employers are looking for when they recruit staff.	Start: 9.00 a.m. Finish: 9.45 a.m.
Succeeding in interviews	Mary Porter develops your interview skills through discussion and role-play.	Start: 10.00 a.m. Finish: 10.45 a.m.
Writing application forms	Local employers give helpful advice and top tips.	Start: 11.30 a.m. Finish: 12.45 p.m.
Setting up your own business	What products or services could you sell? How will you advertise? What else do you need to know? Come and find out!	Start: 1.25 p.m. Finish: 2.00 p.m.
How I set up my own business	Fashion designer Jules Jardine explains how she set up her own business.	Start: 2.15 p.m. Finish: 2.45 p.m.
Get ready for success	Nish Patel shows you how to think positively about your future and make the most of it.	Start: 3.00 p.m. Finish: 4.00 p.m..

For more information, visit our website at www.westerbycollege.ac.uk or call on 01231 770077.

TEXT A2

Jamie buys a book by the fashion designer, Jules Jardine. He reads the contents page.

Rags to Riches

by Jules Jardine

Jules Jardine is an award-winning fashion designer. Jules began designing clothes for her friends at the age of 16. Her exquisite designs are now sold around the world. Jules is a judge on the popular television series, *The Great British Design Challenge*.

Contents

First published by Westerby Books in 2016.

TEXT B1

> Ula is planning a holiday. She reads this web page.

Holiday Time!

Take a coach trip to beautiful Barcelona

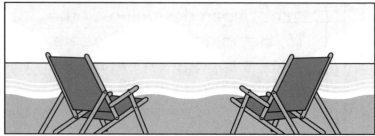

Barcelona is a beautiful city with thousands of things to see and do. It's the perfect city break if you want sun, sea and sight-seeing.

Take a nine day trip to Barcelona and see for yourself. You can enjoy:

- a beautiful beach
- delicious food
- amazing art galleries
- incredible buildings
- great shops.

Home

Hotels

Flights

Car

Deals

Prices

Coach travel only	£179
Coach travel and hotel accommodation	£549
Coach travel and hotel accommodation and activities	£699

Coaches depart from and return to Westerby Coach Station.

For more information, visit **www.westerbycoaches.co.uk** or **call us on 01231 658340**

Westerby Coaches, 19 Station Road, Westerby PT7 9AQ

TEXT B2

Ula books a coach trip to Barcelona. She receives this email.

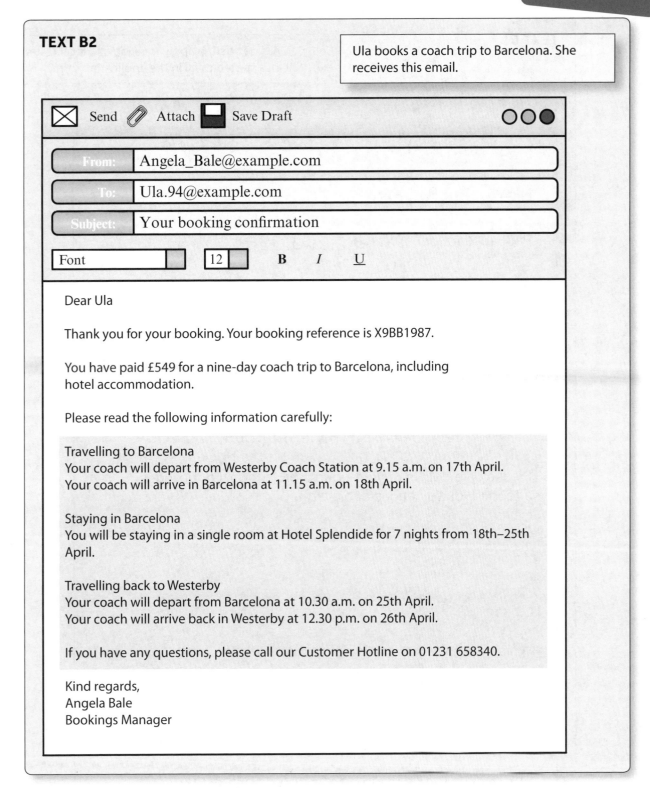

☒ Send   ✐ Attach   ◼ Save Draft   ○ ○ ●

From: Angela_Bale@example.com

To: Ula.94@example.com

Subject: Your booking confirmation

Font ▾   12 ▾   **B**   *I*   <u>U</u>

Dear Ula

Thank you for your booking. Your booking reference is X9BB1987.

You have paid £549 for a nine-day coach trip to Barcelona, including hotel accommodation.

Please read the following information carefully:

Travelling to Barcelona
Your coach will depart from Westerby Coach Station at 9.15 a.m. on 17th April.
Your coach will arrive in Barcelona at 11.15 a.m. on 18th April.

Staying in Barcelona
You will be staying in a single room at Hotel Splendide for 7 nights from 18th–25th April.

Travelling back to Westerby
Your coach will depart from Barcelona at 10.30 a.m. on 25th April.
Your coach will arrive back in Westerby at 12.30 p.m. on 26th April.

If you have any questions, please call our Customer Hotline on 01231 658340.

Kind regards,
Angela Bale
Bookings Manager

TEXT C1

Jen has decided to apply for a job at a local restaurant. She has started to fill in the application form.

Bites Restaurant Application Form

Name: Jen Roberts

Post applied for: Part-time waitress

Address: 72 George Lane,

Westerby   Postcode: JPT18 4TQ

Telephone number: 07700 753 190

Email address: Jenrob@my.email.com

Please give details of your education (schools or colleges attended, qualifications achieved)

Which days are you available for work? Please circle.

Monday   Tuesday Wednesday

Thursday   Friday   Saturday   Sunday

Previous relevant experience:

I used to work in a local newsagent every Saturday, so I am used to serving customers and taking money.

Why are you the right person for this position?

I am studying catering at college at the moment. I want to work in a restaurant so I can find out more about the restaurant business. I am polite and hard-working and always on time.

TEXT C2

Jen receives a letter, inviting her to an interview.

Bites Restaurant
6 High Street,
Westerby,
PO1 9YY
www.biteswesterby.co.uk
Telephone: 01231 33 5555

Ms J Roberts
72 George Lane
Westerby
PT18 4TQ

10th September 2017

Dear Ms Roberts

Thank you for your recent application for the position of part-time waitress.
I am pleased to be able to invite you to an interview at the restaurant on
Tuesday 18th September at 3 p.m. Please arrive in good time and tell one of our
friendly staff that you have come for an interview.

You will be interviewed by:
• Helen Baxter, Restaurant Owner
• Amy Stubbs, Restaurant Manager.

The interview will last approximately 20 minutes.

Please confirm you are able to attend the interview by ringing us on the above
number or by emailing us at amy@biteswesterby.co.uk

We look forward to seeing you next week.

Yours sincerely,

Amy Jones

Amy Jones

TASK A1

You and three friends see this advertisement in the local paper.

COULD YOU AND YOUR FRIENDS SURVIVE IN PARADISE?

We are making a television programme which will follow you and three friends as you try to survive a month stranded on a deserted island.
You will be the only humans on the island.
You will need to find food, water and shelter to survive.
Are you tough enough?

Send your application to
surviveparadise@example.com

You decide to apply. As part of the application you have to write a few sentences explaining why you and your friends would be the right people to take part in the programme.

You could include:
*   why you are interested in this programme
*   why you and your friends would entertain viewers
*   your skills and experience that would help you to survive.

Plan and draft your writing before you write your final response.
In your final response write complete sentences using joining words (conjunctions),
e.g. and, as, but, or.
Check your spellings.
Remember to use capital letters, full stops and question marks where you need to.

(12 marks)

TASK A2

Your friend is starting a new business and has asked you to help her promote her business on social media.

Delicious Desserts
located in Estrick Town Centre

Write an advert for the business which you could post on social media.

You could include:
*   details of your friend's business: the products it sells or the service it provides
*   why customers should use your friend's business
*   anything else customers will need to know.

Write complete sentences using joining words (conjunctions), e.g. and, as, but, or.
Check your spellings.
Remember to use capital letters, full stops and question marks where you need to.

(8 marks)

TASK B1

Your school/college/workplace is organising a Party Night to raise money for a local charity. You have offered to arrange the food for 50 guests to eat at the Party Night.

Write a letter to a local supermarket, asking if they will donate some food to help feed your guests.

You could include:
- details of the event you are organising
- details of the charity you are helping
- the quantity and kinds of food you would like them to donate.

Plan and draft your writing before you write your final response.
In your final response write in complete sentences using joining words (conjunctions), e.g. and, as, but, or.
Check your spellings.
Remember to use capital letters, full stops and question marks where you need to.

(12 marks)

TASK B2

A friend has sent you an email inviting you to go on holiday with them. You are not free on the dates your friend has booked the holiday, so you will not be able to go. Write an email to tell your friend.

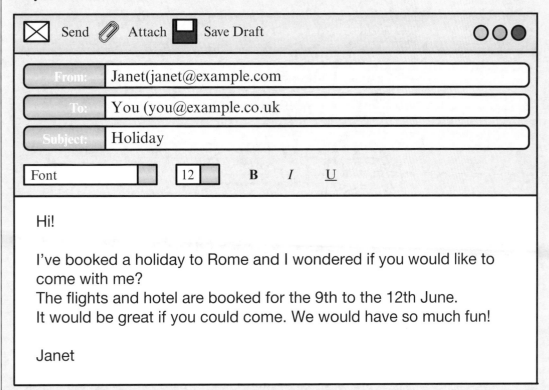

In your email, you could:
- thank your friend for inviting you
- explain why you cannot go on the holiday
- suggest other friends who might like to go on the holiday.

Write complete sentences using joining words (conjunctions), e.g. and, as, but, or.
Check your spellings.
Remember to use capital letters, full stops and question marks where you need to.

(8 marks)

TASK C1

You live on a busy road. There have been two accidents on your road in the past week.

Write a letter to Ms Brown, Head of Roads and Transport at your local council. Ask for the speed limit to be reduced from 30 mph to 20 mph.

In your letter, you could include:
*   details of the accidents that have happened in the past week
*   why you think that slowing down traffic will make your road a safer place to live
*   any other benefits of reducing the speed limit.

Plan and draft your writing before you write your final response.
In your final response write complete sentences using joining words (conjunctions), e.g. and, as, but, or.
Check your spellings.
Remember to use capital letters, full stops and question marks where you need to.

(12 marks)

TASK C2

A relative has sent you an email:

Write a reply, giving your relative some advice.

In your email, you could include:
- information about living and working in your area
- information about going out and things to do in your area
- your advice: should your relative move?

Write complete sentences using joining words (conjunctions), e.g. and, as, but, or.
Check your spellings.
Remember to use capital letters, full stops and question marks where you need to.

(8 marks)

Practice paper: Reading

This practice paper has been written to help you practise what you have learned and may not be representative of a real exam paper.

45 minutes

The total mark for this paper is 20.

INSTRUCTIONS

- Use blue or black ink. Do not use pencil.
- Answer **all** questions.
- Answer the questions in the spaces provided – there may be more space than you need.

Read Text D1 and answer questions 1–5.

Text D1

Rafael goes to Westerby Animal Rescue Centre. He looks at some information about the dogs that need a new home.

WOOF!

Name: Billy
Breed: Labrador
Age: 2 years

Billy is a friendly, lively dog who loves to be with people. He will need a calm, quiet home.

Name: Hattie
Breed: Jack Russell
Age: 6 years

Hattie is a bundle of energy. She will need an experienced owner.

Name: Ethel
Breed: German Shepherd
Age: 4 years

Ethel is not house-trained and has never walked on a lead. Her new owner will need time and patience.

Name: Gemma
Breed: cross breed
Age: 5 months

Gemma is a nervous dog but will soon become more confident with a caring owner.

Name: Russ
Breed: Dalmation
Age: 3 years

Russ is strong but affectionate. He loves to chase so he cannot live with cats.

Name: Patch
Breed: Collie
Age: 3 months

Patch is a very loyal dog so would be happy being the only dog in your home.

Text D1 questions

1   Put a tick ☑ in the correct box.

How old is Russ, the Dalmatian?

☐   **A**   1 year

☐   **B**   2 years

☐   **C**   3 years

☐   **D**   4 years

(1 mark)

2   Put a tick ☑ in the correct box.

What is the name of the only cross-breed dog at the Rescue Centre?

☐   **A**   Gemma

☐   **B**   Ethel

☐   **C**   Russ

☐   **D**   Hattie

(1 mark)

3   Put a tick ☑ in the correct box.

Which dog needs an experienced owner?

☐   **A**   Gemma

☐   **B**   Ethel

☐   **C**   Russ

☐   **D**   Hattie

(1 mark)

4   Put a tick ☑ in the correct box.

Which dog needs a quiet home?

☐   **A**   Billy

☐   **B**   Ethel

☐   **C**   Russ

☐   **D**   Hattie

(1 mark)

5   Put a tick ☑ in the correct box.

Which dog cannot live with cats?

☐   **A**   Gemma

☐   **B**   Ethel

☐   **C**   Russ

☐   **D**   Hattie

(1 mark)

6 Write your answer on the line below.

What is the name of the youngest dog at the rescue centre?

....

(1 mark)

7 Write your answer on the lines below.

Rafael thinks he would like to adopt a German Shepherd. What will Rafael need to have if he decides to adopt the German Shepherd from the Westerby Animal Rescue Centre?

....

....

(1 mark)

8 Write your answer on the line below.

What breed of dog is Hattie?

....

(1 mark)

9 Write your answer on the line below.

Which dog is not house-trained?

....

(1 mark)

10 Write your answer on the line below.

What is the name of the oldest dog at the rescue centre?

....

(1 mark)

Read Text D2 and answer questions 6–9.

Text D2

Rafael reads a leaflet from the Animal Rescue Centre.

CHOOSING YOUR DOG

Choosing the right dog to adopt can be difficult. These are some of the things you need to think about.

What breed should I choose?

The most important thing is to choose a breed that suits you. There are lively breeds that need lots of time and energy. There are quiet, placid breeds that spend more time snoozing. Think about the dog's personality as well as its looks!

What should I know?

Ask lots of questions about our dogs. We can give you lots of information about each dog's character and habits so you can be sure it's the right dog for you.

What do we need to know?

What kind of home do you live in? Is someone at home all day? Do you have other dogs? Do you have other pets? If you tell us all about your home, we can help you to find the right dog for you.

Text D2 questions

11   Put a tick ☑ in the correct box.

According to Text D2, what is the most important thing to do when you choose a dog?

☐   **A**   choose a breed that suits you

☐   **B**   choose a breed that looks good

☐   **C**   choose a breed that is popular

☐   **D**   choose a breed that is quiet

(1 mark)

12   Put a tick ☑ in the correct box.

According to Text D2, what can the Rescue Centre give you lots of information about?

☐   **A**   how to train your new dog

☐   **B**   how to look after your new dog

☐   **C**   each dog's character and habits

☐   **D**   each dog's previous owners

(1 mark)

13 Put a tick ☑ in the correct box.

According to Text D2, what do lively breeds of dog need?

☐ **A** a friend

☐ **B** lots of time and energy

☐ **C** a sleep

☐ **D** lots of water

(1 mark)

14 Put a tick ☑ in the correct box.

According to Text D2, what do placid breeds of dog spend their time doing?

☐ **A** barking

☐ **B** running around

☐ **C** snoozing

☐ **D** drinking

(1 mark)

15 Write your answer on the lines below.

Write down **two** things that the Rescue Centre staff need to know so that they can help you find the right dog for you.

....

....

(2 marks)

16 Write your answer on the lines below.

Look up the word 'placid' in the dictionary and write down what it means.

....

....

(1 mark)

17 Write your answer on the lines below.

When you're choosing a dog to adopt, what should you think about as well as how it looks?

....

....

(1 mark)

18 Write your answer on the lines below.

Look up the word 'habit' in the dictionary and write down what it means.

....

....

(1 mark)

19 Write your answer on the lines below.

Rafael would like to adopt a dog that suits him. What does Rafael need to tell the Rescue Centre staff about so they can help him?

....

....

(1 mark)

Practice paper: Writing

This practice paper has been written to help you practise what you have learned and may not be representative of a real exam paper.

45 minutes

The total mark for this paper is 20.

INSTRUCTIONS
- Use blue or black ink. Do not use pencil.
- Answer **all** questions.
- Answer the questions in the spaces provided – there may be more space than you need.

Task 1

Three different companies are trying to buy a large piece of land near where you live.

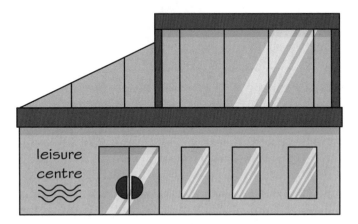

- One company wants to build a new cinema.
- Another company wants to build a new shopping centre.
- A third company wants to build a new sports centre.

The piece of land is big enough for only one of these buildings.

Write a letter to Susie Jacobs, the head of your local council, giving your views on which of the three buildings would be best for the community.

In your letter you could include:

- which of the three buildings you would choose
- the reasons for your choice
- anything else you think the council should know.

Plan and draft your writing before you write your final response.
In your final response write complete sentences using joining words, (conjunctions) e.g. and, as, but, or.

Check your spellings.

Remember to use capital letters, full stops and question marks where you need to.

(12 marks)

Task 2

You have received this email from a distant relative.

Write a reply, explaining why it will not be possible for your relative, his wife and six children to stay with you.

In your email, you could:

• apologise for not being able to welcome them

• explain why it will cause problems if they come to stay

• suggest where else they could stay.

Write complete sentences using joining words (conjunctions), e.g. and, as, but, or.

Check your spellings.

Remember to use capital letters, full stops and question marks where you need to.

(8 marks)

ANSWERS

READING

1. Your reading test

1 B

2 two

3 Read over and check your work.

4 Answers may include three of the following:
- you have answered all the questions
- you have read the questions properly
- you have given the correct amount of information for each answer.

5 B

6 You could use it to look up the meaning of any word you do not understand. You could be asked to look up a word in a dictionary and write down its meaning.

2. Reading the question

1   5 Text A2

    6 Text B2

    7 Text B1

2 B

3 For example:

In Text B2, what will be the date when Ula gets to Barcelona?

4 For example:

In Text B1, where do you get on the coach when you are travelling to Barcelona?

3. Finding the main idea

1 The most useful parts are the introduction, the title and the first sentence.

2 notice

3 This text gives the reader information about an Enterprise Day at Westerby College.

4 Text B1 is a web page from a website.

5 It is about taking a coach trip to Barcelona.

4. Underlining key words

1 3, 1, 2

2 perfect city break

3 There is no model answer for this question. Make sure you have underlined the key words in the text.

4 A

5. Finding details

1 A

2 right person for this job

3 There is no model answer for this question. Make sure you have underlined the key words in the text.

4 C

6. Using a dictionary

1 (a) 4th

  (b) 1st

  (c) 3rd

  (d) 2nd

2 abduct: to take away illegally or kidnap

humerus: a bone in the arm, extending from shoulder to elbow

palatable: having a pleasant or acceptable taste

ululate: to howl or shout

3 For example:

very beautiful.

7. Choosing an answer

1 A

2 (a) No. This student has ticked two boxes. They should have crossed one out.

  (b) C is the correct answer. The tick for answer B should be crossed out.

8. Writing your own answer

1 (a) (b) (c) (d) are all true; (e) is false.

2 (a) B

  (b) Student A's answer is incorrect. Student C has not answered the question in full.

9. Putting it into practice

1 B

2 C

10. Headings and sub-headings

1 Text B1 is a text about a holiday coach trip to Barcelona.

Text B2 is an email confirming a booking for something.

2 (a) B

  (b) C

11. Paragraphs and bullet points

1 (a) 2

  (b) 1

  (c) 3

2 They make a text easier to read by separating important information out into smaller chunks.

3 C

12. Tables and timetables

1 (a) talks and workshops

  (b) times

  (c) details

2 (a) B

  (b) C

13. Forms

1 post applied for

2 A

3 previous relevant experience

4 'Please give details of your education' and 'Which days are you available for work?'

14. Putting it into practice

1 B

2 B

3 *The Great British Design Challenge*

4 2016

WRITING

15. Your writing test

1 & 2

(a) and (e) are true.

(b) is false. You will only be asked to plan and draft the first of the two tasks.

(c) is false. You should plan both writing tasks.

(d) is false. The first writing task is worth more marks because your plan and draft will be marked.

3 A, B, C, E, F, H

16. Reading the question

1 the kind of text you are writing: advert

who you are writing to: social media

why you are writing: to help her promote her business

2 (a) There is no model answer for this task. Make sure you have circled all the key words in Task C1.

(b) what you are writing about: the speed limit to be reduced

the kind of text you are writing: a letter

who you are writing to: Ms Brown, Head of Roads and transport at your local council

why you are writing: asking for the speed limit to be reduced from 30 mph to 20 mph

17. Reasons for writing

1 (a) inform and persuade the reader.

(b) inform and explain to the reader.

2 (a) For example: I have read the advert and I think I would like to try using this new business.

(b) For example: I have read the email and I think it is a pity my friend can't come on holiday.

3 For example: The reason for writing Task A1 is to inform the reader about me and my friends and persuade them we would be the best people to go on their programme. I want the reader to think they would be really interesting to watch on the programme.

18. Who you are writing to

1 Ideas A, C and F are not relevant to the reader. All other ideas are relevant.

2 & 3 There is no model answer for this question. Make sure you have included several relevant ideas.

19. Planning

1 There is no model answer for this question. Make sure you have included one relevant idea for each bullet point.

2 There is no model answer for this question. Make sure you have included some relevant responses to the key questions.

3 (a) **What** skills have we got that would help us survive on the island?

(b) **Where** did we get these skills?

(c) **When** will we be going to the island?

(d) **Why** would we be the best people to appear on the programme?

(e) **How** would we entertain viewers?

20. Organising

1 For example:

[1]	Thanks for the invite.	[6]	I need the money!
[4]	I can't go in June.	[8]	Ant said he wanted to go on a sunny holiday.
[5]	My dad's paying me to paint his house in June.		
[7]	I promised him and I can't let him down.	[3]	I bet you'll have a great time.
[2]	I wish I could come.	[9]	I'm jealous!

2 (a) There is no model answer for this question. Make sure you have included several relevant ideas.

(b) There is no model answer for this question. Make sure you have numbered your ideas in a logical order.

21. Drafting

1 All four are important reasons for drafting.

2 To mark a new paragraph: //

To mark a word you want to insert: ^

An asterisk: *

22. Checking

1

Hi ~~jem~~ Jem

I ~~wont~~ won't be able to come to ~~tenerife~~ Tenerife with you next month because ~~im~~ I'm going to be ~~to~~ too busy working.

~~its~~ It's really annoying and ~~i'm~~ I'm gutted but ~~their~~ there are loads ~~of~~ people who would like to ~~go you~~ go. You should ask ~~adam~~ Adam and ~~baz~~ Baz because I don't think ~~their~~ they're ~~busy i~~ busy. I bet they'd love it.

~~all~~ All the best

Dai

2 Make sure you check your work for common mistakes.

23. Putting it into practice

There is no model answer for this question. Your draft response should be planned and organised carefully and not contain any of the common mistakes you have highlighted previously.

24. Writing an email

1 The first is too formal. The second is too informal. The third is just right.

2 For example:

Hi Maz

That's great news! I think you should definitely move here because it's a great place to live and there's loads of work and loads to do. I love it here. I think you would too.

All the best

Dan

25. Writing a letter

1 the date

2 All options should be crossed out except: Ms Brown / Yours sincerely.

3 For example:

~~I'm~~ I am writing to ask you to ~~drop~~ lower the speed limit on my road to 20 mph. ~~There's~~ There have been two accidents on my road in the past week. People ~~got~~ were hurt and one was a seven-year-old ~~kid~~ child.

People drive down our road much too ~~quick~~ quickly. This is what causes accidents and it makes our road dangerous and noisy. I think you should definitely make the speed limit lower.

26. Writing instructions

1 For example:

Hold the hammer in your right hand. Hold the nail in place with your left hand. Hit the head of the nail with the hammer. Make sure you do not hit your fingers!

2 For example:

<u>Next,</u> remove the tablet from its packaging.

<u>Then</u> place the tablet at the back of your tongue.

<u>Finally,</u> take a large sip of water, tipping your head back as you swallow it.

27. Writing a report

1 For example:

I have been asked to write this report suggesting different kinds of event we could hold to raise money for a local charity.

2 For example:

(a) What could we do?

(b) Which one should we do?

(c) How should we do it?

3 There is no model answer for this question. Make sure you have included relevant ideas with the sub-headings you wrote for question 2.

28. Writing a notice or advert

1 A

2 heading, information, contact details

3 For example:

<u>Where</u> can I find this product? <u>How</u> do I contact this business? <u>When</u> is this product or service available?

29. Writing a personal statement

1 B

2 There is no model answer for this question. Make sure you have included four relevant ideas.

3 **(b)** Write complete sentences.

(c) Use formal language.

(d) Use correct punctuation and grammar.

30. Putting it into practice

Emails: Suitable greeting and sign-off, paragraphs, language relevant for audience

Letters: The date on the top right, a greeting on the left, formal language, a sign-off followed by your name

Instructions: Clear language, concise sentences, command verbs, numbered lists or time indicators

Reports: An introduction, bullet point lists to break up information, formal language

Notices or adverts: A relevant heading, important information

Personal statements: Formal language, why you are interested, why you are the right person

31. Paragraphs

1 **(a)** and **(d)** are false. **(b) (c)** and **(e)** are true.

2 **(a)** C

(b) The ideas can be grouped into three sections. You can use the bullet points in the writing task to guide your planning and your paragraphing.

32. Sentences

1 A, C and D

2 **(a)** ~~we~~ We are organising a party night at Westerby College on 18th ~~September we~~ September. We are going to be raising money for the new Day Centre for elderly ~~people~~ people.

(b) ~~the~~ The Day Centre will help old people to get out of the house and make new ~~friends it's~~ friends. It's a really worthwhile ~~cause we're~~ cause. We're hoping to raise over a thousand ~~pounds~~ pounds.

(c) ~~we~~ We would like you to donate food to help the party and help the elderly people of ~~Westerby we~~ Westerby. We would be very grateful and so would ~~they~~ they.

3 For example:

Do you enjoy <u>tasty</u> desserts? Delicious desserts has a <u>huge</u> selection of <u>very</u> sweet treats just for you. We <u>always</u> use locally sourced ingredients. Next time you're in Estrick Town Centre, come and try our <u>extremely</u> delicious desserts!

33. Talking about the present

1 **(a)** am, think

(b) speed

(c) travel

(d) worry, think, is, live

(e) are, do

(f) are

2 **(b)** was

(c) had

(d) were

(e) loved

3 **(b)** There is a great choice of shops.

(c) It has a cinema and a sports centre.

(d) The people are very friendly.

(e) I love it.

34. Making the verb match

1 **(a)** verb = got; subject = I

(b) verb = was; subject = Your email

(c) verb = knew; subject = Nobody

2 **(a)** are

(b) am

(c) is

(d) is

(e) are

3
(a) are

(b) have

(c) build

(d) is

(e) get, argue

35. Talking about the past

1 (a) wrote

(b) tried, answered

(c) slammed

(d) rang, hurried

(e) hoped

2 (b) were

(c) were

(d) were

(e) was

3 (a) I went to college one day a week.

(b) I brought my own lunch to college.

(c) I took sandwiches and a drink.

36. Talking about the future

1 (b) I will work Saturdays and Sundays. / I am going to work Saturdays and Sundays.

(c) I will be a postman delivering parcels to people's houses. / I am going to be a postman delivering parcels to people's houses.

2 (b) I am about to start looking for a new job.

(c) I am about to start my own business.

37. Using joining words

1 For example:

(a) We love camping <u>and</u> we go every year.

(b) We go for a week <u>or</u> sometimes we go for a fortnight.

(c) We spend all our time together <u>but</u> we never argue.

(d) Viewers would enjoy our banter <u>and</u> they would watch the programme every week.

2 For example:

(a) We love camping when the sun shines / until it starts raining. We go every year.

(b) We go for a week so we can relax / because it is quite far away. Sometimes we go for a fortnight so we can do more things.

(c) We spend all our time together although sometimes we take a solo walk / if we go out for the day. We never argue because we're very close.

(d) Viewers would enjoy our banter because we have a lot of fun together / as we are very entertaining. They would watch the programme every week if we were on it.

38. Putting it into practice

There is no model answer for this question. Check your response includes all of the items in the checklist on page 38.

39. Capital letters

1 (b) names of people and places

(c) when you talk about yourself as 'I'

(d) titles of films, books, etc.

(e) months of the year

2

17 <u>S</u>now <u>H</u>ill

<u>W</u>esterby

<u>PO</u>19 4<u>HH</u>

4th <u>N</u>ovember 2016

<u>D</u>ear <u>G</u>ramps

<u>I</u>'ve just watched that old <u>J</u>ames <u>B</u>ond film you said was really good called <u>G</u>oldfinger. <u>I</u>t was pretty good.

3 There is no model answer for this question. Make sure you have written three complete, relevant sentences.

40. Ending a sentence

1 (c) (d) and (e) are correctly punctuated.

2 (a) (b) and (e) should have a question mark not a full stop at the end.

3 I've lived here all my ~~life, I've~~ life. I've never wanted to move away because it's where all my friends and family are. It's got great places to go out, great shops and great places to eat ~~out who~~ out. Who wouldn't want to live in a place like ~~this~~ this?

41. Putting it into practice

There is no model answer for this question. Check your response against the items in the checklist on page 41.

42. Spelling tips

1 (a) when

(b) thumb

(c) could

(d) knee

(e) should

(f) wrong

(g) why

(h) knock

(i) what

(j) doubt

2 (a) valley

(b) suddenly

(c) definitely

(d) sincerely

(e) completely

(f) ugly

(g) nearly

(h) likely

(i) lonely

3 (a) disappoint

(b) disappear

(c) difficult

(d) necessary

(e) tomorrow

(f) different

(g) possible

(h) success

(i) immediate

(j) beginning

4 Make sure you practise spelling any words that you find difficult to remember.

43. Plurals

1 **(a)** lunches

(b) wishes

(c) countries

(d) families

(e) days

(f) boys

2 **(a)** If a word ends in 'ch', 'sh', 'x', 's' or 'ss', you make it plural by adding 'es'.

(b) If a word ends in a consonant (any letter that is not a vowel) and then a 'y', you make it plural by replacing the 'y' with 'ies'.

(c) If a word ends in a vowel (a, e, i, o or u) and then 'y', you make it plural by adding 's'.

3 **(a)** bodies

(b) babies

(c) ways

(d) journeys

(e) glasses

(f) fish

44. Prefixes

1 A2: dislike; B5: immature; C4: incorrect; D3: misunderstand

2 **(a)** disappear

(b) unnecessary

(c) misspell

(d) always

(e) disappoint

(f) altogether

(g) mistake

(h) dissatisfied

45. Suffixes

1 For example:

(a) cooked, cooker, cooking, cookable

(b) enjoyed, enjoying, enjoyable, enjoyment

(c) slowed, slower, slowing, slowest, slowness

2 **(a)** stopping

(b) begged

(c) happier

(d) heaviest

(e) having

(f) making

3 **(a)** When you add a suffix to **most** shorter root words that end with a single consonant, you double that final consonant. **However**, words ending in two consonants remain unchanged, e.g. 'faster'.

(b) When you add **most** suffixes to a root word whose last two letters are a consonant then a 'y', the 'y' changes to 'i'. **However**, when you add the suffix '-ing', the 'y' does not change, e.g. 'hurrying', 'trying'.

(c) When you add a suffix that begins with a vowel to a word ending in 'e', you usually (but not always) take the 'e' off the end of the word.

46. Tricky spellings 1

1 <u>Where</u> I work, all <u>of</u> us have to <u>wear</u> overalls. <u>They're</u> comfortable and keep paint <u>off</u> our clothes. <u>We're</u> in trouble if we don't. <u>There</u> are some new supervisors <u>there</u> who keep <u>their</u> eyes on us all the time. The old supervisors <u>were</u> much nicer.

2 **(b)** there: to do with place or position

(c) they're: an abbreviation of 'they are'

(d) we're: an abbreviation of 'we are'

(e) were: the past tense of 'are' – you are/you were

(f) wear: what you do with clothes

(g) where: a question word, asking about a place

(h) of: belonging to

(i) off: the opposite of 'on'

47. Tricky spellings 2

1 **(a)** There are <u>two</u> different countries I am interested in.

(b) I am interested in going <u>to</u> America and I would like to visit France <u>too</u>.

2 Both of <u>our</u> dogs <u>are</u> house trained.

3 **(a)** I don't <u>know</u> any good plumbers in this town.

(b) There used to be lots of them, but there are no good plumbers <u>now</u>.

4 **(a)** I <u>bought</u> some crisps at the supermarket.

(b) I <u>brought</u> them home and ate them.

48. Tricky spellings 3

1 thought

2 straight

3 sight

4 difficult

5 disappear

6 beginning

7 definite

8 separate

9 different

10 because

11 people

12 remember

13 believe

14 friend

15 piece

16 business

17 decide

18 decision

49. Putting it into practice

There is no model answer for this question. Remember to check your work for misspelled words.

62. Practice paper: Reading

Practice test answers
Reading

1 C
2 A
3 D
4 A
5 C
6 Gemma
7 time and patience
8 Jack Russell
9 Ethel
10 Hattie
11 A
12 C
13 B
14 C
15 Any two of the following:
  - What kind of home do you live in?
  - Is someone at home all day?
  - Do you have other dogs?
  - Do you have other pets?
16 not easily upset or excited; calm and peaceful
17 personality
18 something that you do often and regularly
19 his home

66. Practice paper: Writing

There are no model answers for these tasks. Make sure you have:
- included plenty of ideas, addressing all of the task bullet points
- written in complete sentences
- ordered your ideas logically
- included extra details to make your writing interesting.

You should use formal language for Task 1 and fairly informal language for Task 2.

Notes

Notes

Published by Pearson Education Limited, 80 Strand, London, WC2R 0RL.

www.pearsonschoolsandfecolleges.co.uk

Copies of official specifications for all Edexcel qualifications may be found on the website: www.edexcel.com

Text © Pearson Education Limited 2017
Edited, typeset and produced by Elektra Media Ltd
Original illustrations © Pearson Education Limited 2017
Illustrated by Elektra Media Ltd
Cover illustration by Miriam Sturdee

The right of David Grant to be identified as author work of this has been asserted by him in accordance with the Copyright, Designs and Patents Act 1988.

First published 2017

20 19 18 17
10 9 8 7 6 5 4 3 2 1

British Library Cataloguing in Publication Data
A catalogue record for this book is available from the British Library

ISBN 978 1 292 14573 0

Printed in Slovakia by Neografia